THE TASTY
NUMBER TWELVE

Written by Dave Tovey
Illustrated by Jaimee Christensen & Bruce Martin

3 lions and 3 giraffes and 3 elephants and 3 camels make . . .

. . . 12 cookies.

4 hearts and 4 stars
and 4 moons make . . .

. . . 12 cookies.

6 boys and 6 girls
make 12 children and . . .

. . . no cookies!